KU-724-503

THE
PHONE

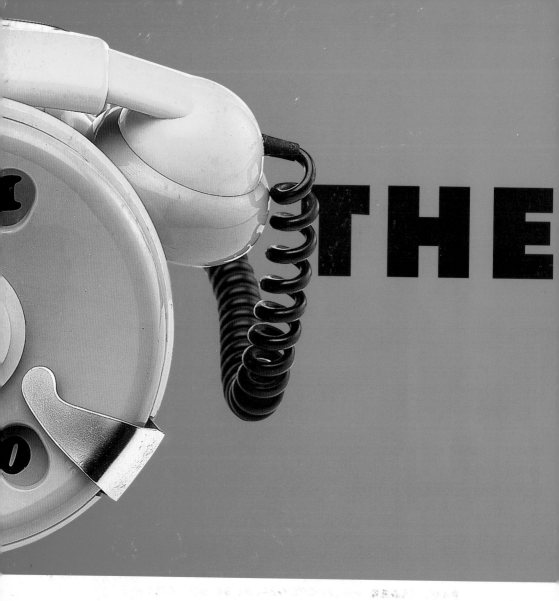

THE

PHONE

AN APPRECIATION

AURUM PRESS

PAUL CLARK ◉ PHOTOGRAPHS BY GUY RYECART

First published in Great Britain 1997 by
Aurum Press Limited, 25 Bedford Avenue,
London WC1B 2AT

A catalogue record for this book
is available from the British Library

ISBN 1 85410 529 9

This book was conceived,
designed and produced by
THE IVY PRESS LIMITED
2/3 St Andrews Place, Lewes,
East Sussex BN7 1UP

Art Director: Peter Bridgewater
Commissioning Editor: Viv Croot
Managing Editor: Anne Townley
Editors: Graham Smith, Julie Whitaker
Page layout: Ron Bryant-Funnell
Photography: Guy Ryecart

Printed and bound in China

Throughout this book the dimensions of
the objects are given in imperial and metric
measurements; height, width and depth are
expressed by H, W and D.

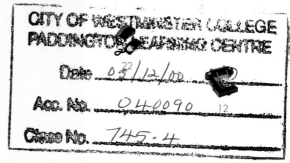

15

23

30

15

25

20

11

29

24

19

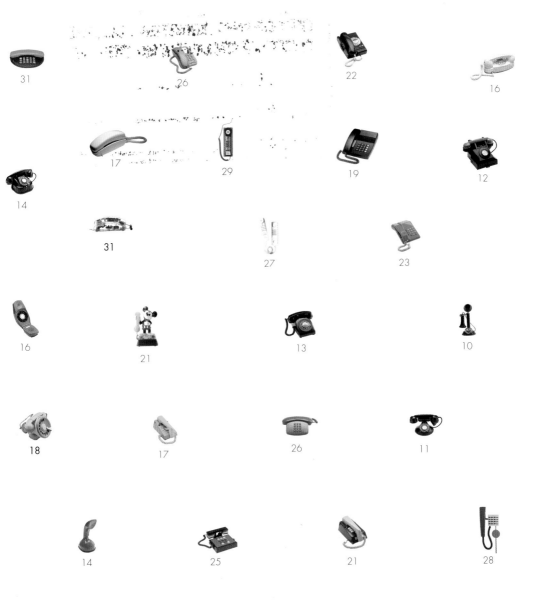

31

26

22

16

17

29

19

12

14

31

27

23

16

21

13

10

18

17

26

11

14

25

21

28

Introduction

It is difficult to imagine present-day life without the convenience of a telephone. It has become a necessity – the carrier of every kind of communication, from family news to crucial business deals, from the take-away pizza order to a President's message to his astronauts.

Bobophone
Tecler, 1970s

The familiar phone, with its connection to a wall socket and its solid handpiece, is now in competition with the mobile and cordless varieties, but its future seems secure nonetheless. The electronic revolution that it fostered (Bell Telephone Laboratories invented the transistor in 1948) continues to provide it with ever more user-friendly features, and it still wins our vote for reliability, sound quality and relatively low cost.

The telephone was a logical development of the electric telegraph – and we still refer to the poles that

Ericofon 600
Ericsson, 1954

Siemens TIS 282
Siemens, 1960s

carry the telephone wires as 'telegraph poles'. There are several contenders for the title of inventor of the telephone, but Alexander Graham Bell is the front-runner.

Siemens 200 series
1929

Despite its crudity, his telephone worked, causing an absolute sensation at the 1876 Centennial Exhibition at Philadelphia, where the Emperor of Brazil famously exclaimed, 'My God, it talks!' when it was demonstrated to him.

Its obvious potential for business and domestic use attracted huge investment, and many improvements were made in order to get round Bell's patents, including those by Edison, who invented the carbon

Bell's 'Gallows'
1876

microphone and the separate mouth- and earpieces. The superiority of the telephone over the telegram for commercial and personal communications was quickly realized, and telephone systems expanded rapidly in the newly industrialized world of the early 20th century. The number of telegrams sent each

year in Britain dropped from 80 million in 1915 to just 33 million in 1935.

Bell's first telephones were rectangular wooden boxes with a combined speaker and earpiece at one end, looking remarkably like a camera. When the

GPO Pedestal
1920

Edison Wall set
c.1879

earpiece and mouthpiece became separate devices, two main table-telephone shapes emerged – the combined handpiece sitting in a cradle on top of the apparatus, and the 'candlestick' type, with the microphone at the top and the earpiece on a separate cord hanging on the side switch (thereby giving us the phrase 'to hang up').

As well as the personal table or desk set, there was also the wall phone. When combined with a coin-box apparatus, this became the public telephone, or pay station, and the early 20th century saw the development of the telephone kiosk. Meanwhile, in the home the wall phone developed into a piece of furniture. The handsome apparatus of the Ericsson wall phone graced the hallway of many a Victorian and Edwardian upper middle-class home.

Ericsson Wall Telephone
c.1900

Early phones were made from combinations of traditional materials – pressed, cast and turned metals, turned wood, glass and porcelain, but the arrival of plastic moulding in the 1920s gave the telephone its classic shape and opened the door to mass consumption. The first moulded phones were in dark phenolic plastics such as Bakelite, but colours arrived with the use of urea formaldehydes and cellulose

Grillo
Siemens, Italy, 1965

acetate. More recently, most phones have been made in the light, strong and easily coloured ABS (Acrylonitrile Butadiene Styrene) plastic.

For the first 60 years, telephone design was largely in the hands of engineers, but as competition became more intense, manufacturers

**Ericsson 'skeleton' set
for the Rothschilds**
c.1900

called on the services of the newly arrived industrial designers.

Recent technological advances, particularly the miniaturization of electronic components, have offered designers new possibilities of form and shape, resulting in some very fine designs and a host of telephones disguised as anything from a banana to a high-heeled shoe.

EPSOM

The 'Epsom', though sounding very English, was in fact imported from the USA. In an age when the 'talkies' hadn't yet been invented, the 'candlestick' gave an increasing number of telephone users the opportunity for some aural entertainment. Halfway between the early candlestick type and a dial handset, it required you to sit next to it, or to use both hands.

c. 1912, H11.25 X W6 X D5.25IN / H28.5 X W15.2 X D13.3CM

UREA FORMALDEHYDE, 1929,
H7 X W9 X D6.4IN / H17.8 X W22.8 X D16.2CM

BAKELITE, 1930S,
H5 X W9 X D5.75IN / H12.7 X W22.8 X D14.6CM

NEOPHONE

SIEMENS

The elegant and appropriately named 'Neophone' coincided with a period of great expansion in phone ownership. The first phone case to be made completely in Bakelite, it was available in a range of colours as well as black, but the colours commanded a premium rental in Great Britain, where it was called the '162'.

STROWGER DIAL SET

ALMON STROWGER

Almon Strowger, an undertaker by trade, invented the first effective automatic telephone exchange in 1891 to thwart a competitor whom he thought was being tipped off by the local phone operator. His rotating finger dial remained an essential feature of the handset until it was replaced by the push-button phone in the 1960s.

TYPE 300
'CHEESEDISH'
GPO/ERICSSON/JEAN HEIBERG

Sculptor Jean Heiberg created one of the classic telephone designs for Ericsson of Sweden – subsequently licensed to be made throughout the world. It was introduced to Britain with style by the Prince of Wales, who had seen it on his travels. Like the 'Neophone', the 'Cheesedish' was mainly made in Bakelite and came to symbolize the archetypal telephone in most people's minds.

BAKELITE, 1930,
H5.75 X W5 X D7.75IN / H14.6 X W12.7 X D19.7CM

BAKELITE, 1940S,
H5.75 X W5 X D7.75IN / H14.6 X W12.7 X D19.7CM

TYPE 300
GPO/ERICSSON/JEAN HEIBERG

In the dark days of the Second World War telephonic communication provided a vital link for the military, and a lifeline for separated civilians. Churchill would have issued top-secret orders on a Type 300 phone like this, and would have used the secret button when necessary to 'scramble' the conversation.

BELL TYPE 500

WESTERN ELECTRIC/HENRY
DREYFUSS ASSOCIATES

In the postwar economic boom, a new style of phone was needed to cater for the 50 million US subscribers. Bell Telephone Laboratories (AT&T) commissioned Henry Dreyfuss Associates, who came up with the no-nonsense Type 500. Conservative in taste, it became the world leader in style, dominating the US office and home phone market – despite being available only in black!

BAKELITE, 1949,
H5 X W9 X D8.25IN
H12.7 X W22.8 X D21CM

BAKELITE, MID-1950S,
H5.25 X W9 X D5.5IN
H13.3 X W22.9 X D14CM

ACRYLIC, 1954,
H8.25 X W4.75 X D3.75IN
H21.7 X W12 X D9.5CM

ERICOFON 600
ERICSSON/RALPH LYSELL

Ericsson was pre-eminent in phone manufacture for over half a century and surprised the world with this revolutionary single-piece phone in 1954 (originally designed by Ralph Lysell in 1941). Called the Erica in the U.S.A. and aimed specifically at the housewife market, it was mocked for being distinctly phallic (especially the vibrant red version!).

RTT STANDARD TELEPHONE

Practically every European country developed its own standard phone style or adopted one of the Ericsson or Siemens designs in the 1950s. Inspector Maigret would have used a Belgian phone like this one. The bar at the front hinges up, making it one of the first phones since the "candlestick" to be designed for carrying around while speaking.

CELLULOSE ACETATE, 1958,
H4.7 X W8.75 X D10IN / H12 X W22.2 X D25.4CM

ABS PLASTIC, 1959,
H4.8 X W9.5 X D8.5IN / H12.2 X W24.1 X D21.6CM

NIZZOLI 2+7

SAFNAT/MARCELLO NIZZOLI

Although primarily intended as an office intercom, this light-hearted design by Marcello Nizzoli showed how friendly the telephone could be. Plastics technology had come a long way from the limited possibilities of Bakelite, and cellulose acetate now opened the door to this jolly blue version. Could the Audrey Hepburn 1957 film *Funny Face* have inspired this design?

TYPE 700

ERICSSON/GPO/W. J. AVERY

Heralding the 1960s, a new British phone with a softer shape, new electronic components, and a range of six colors met the expectations of the new design-conscious consumer. You still couldn't own your own, though – you had to rent it! The 700 series was designed for the GPO by W. J. Avery of Ericsson, but owed a distinct debt to the Bell 500.

ABS PLASTIC, 1959
H3 X W8.25 X D3.25IN / H7.7 X W21 X D8.2CM

ABS PLASTIC, 1965, H2.75 X W2.75 X D6.5IN / H7 X W7 X D16.5CM

THE PRINCESS BELL

BELL/WESTERN ELECTRIC/HENRY DREYFUSS

The telephone was a neutral, genderless object until the need for an 'extra' phone in the boom days of the late 1950s resulted in the concept of a 'feminine'-styled phone. Black was abandoned for pale pastel plastic and the word 'dainty' was used for the first time to describe a telephone.

GRILLO

SIEMENS ITALY/ SAPPER AND ZANUSO

Here the telephone is reduced to nothing but the handset. By separating the ringer and putting it back on the wall where it had originally been, Richard Sapper and Marco Zanuso designed the revolutionary and prize-winning folding 'Grillo' (Cricket) phone, which evokes the form of natural objects. Closing its shell cuts off the line and ends the call.

ABS PLASTIC, 1968,
H2.75 X W2.75 X D9IN / H7 X W7 D22.8CM

TRIMLINE
BELL/WESTERN ELECTRIC/DON GENARO AT HENRY DREYFUSS

Continuing the horizontal visual theme started with the Princess, and maintaining their position as telephone innovators, Bell achieved the single-piece phone, first with a dial and later with push-buttons in the handpiece itself, made possible by the miniaturization of electronic parts. This coincided with a new generation of 'Touch Tone' pulse dialling systems, which provided useful extra services that we now take for granted.

TRIMPHONE (DIAL VERSION)
STC/MARTYN ROWLANDS

Designed by Martyn Rowlands, the angular Trimphone was revolutionary and among the first in the UK to have the handset covering the dial. Originally designed as a bedside phone, it was half the weight of the traditional phone, could be lifted up by its handset rest and had a dial that was illuminated by radioactive Tritium gas. Later models came in two-tone colour schemes chosen by Lord Snowdon.

ABS PLASTIC, 1966,
H4.25 X W4.25 X D8IN
H10.8 X W10.8 X D20.3CM

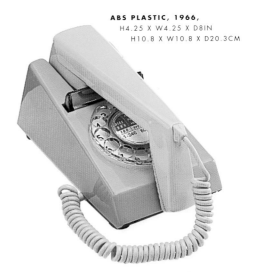

ABS PLASTIC,
EARLY 1970S,
H6.25 X W9 X D7.9IN
H15.6 X W22.8 X D20CM

BOBOPHONE

TECLER

If the 1970s were about flamboyance, the two-tone Italian Bobophone pulled out all the stops and dramatically symbolized the mood of the times, with its alarm-clock-style external bells and an oversized dial. Imported into the UK by Standard Telephones & Cables, it was also available in plum and magenta – another very typical 1970s' combination.

ERICOFON 700

L. M. ERICSSON

ABS PLASTIC, 1976,
H3.25 X W7.75 X D9IN / H8.3 X W19.7 X D22.8CM

For their centennial in 1976, Ericsson re-launched an updated version of the Ericofon, with advanced solid-state electronics, a more angular 1970s' shape and a push-button dialler located in the base. It was available in grey, red, cream, green and blue.

ABS PLASTIC, 1976,
H8.25 X W3.4 X D4IN
H21.7 X W8.6 X D10CM

COMET

KIRK ALCATEL/JAKOB JENSEN

Originally called the Digitel 2000, this elegant design by Jakob Jensen has been described as 'timeless'. Having enjoyed worldwide success and been in continuous production for over 20 years, the Comet has the honour of being in the permanent collection of the Museum of Modern Art in New York.

ABS PLASTIC, 1977,

H4.5 X W9 X D4IN / H11.4 X W22.9 X D10.2CM

COMPACT

BT/STC/DAVID CARTER ASSOCIATES

The compact phone, designed by David Carter, was created in response to the need for small domestic telephones. A special limited edition in Balmoral Blue was made to celebrate Queen Elizabeth's Silver Jubilee in 1977. Like the Italian Grillo, its minimal dimensions were achieved by separating the bell from the handset.

MICKEY MOUSE

**AMERICAN
TELECOMMUNICATION CORP.**

ABS PLASTIC, 1979,
H4.25 X W4.25 X D8IN
H10.8 X W10.8 X D20.3CM

Pop Art had made its mark on the fine arts in the 1960s, and by the 1970s a desire for irreverent style turned the tide against the dull convention of the predictable product. Accompanied by Snoopy, this was the definitive 1970s' fun phone, its form owing much to the original 'candlestick' design.

ABS PLASTIC, 1978,
H15 X W8.5 X D8.5IN / H38.1 X W21.6 X D21.6CM

DELTA (PUSH BUTTON VERSION)

**STC/MARTYN
ROWLANDS**

This version was a logical advance on its sister phone (see page 17), following the arrival of pulse signals. It, too, enjoyed enormous popularity and was one of the first push-button devices to be widely distributed. Instead of a bell, the Delta had an electronic tone caller with adjustable volume.

ABS PLASTIC, 1979,
H3 X W5.25 X D9IN / H7.6 X W13.3 X D22.8CM

ABS PLASTIC, 1981,
H3 X W5 X D9IN
H7.6 X W12.7 X D22.8CM

CITESA

BILL MOGGRIDGE ASSOCIATES

The consumer boom of the late 1970s, and the improvement in most European infrastructures, created a great demand for new phone designs. Bill Moggridge Associates in Britain originally designed this phone for the Spanish phone manufacturer CITESA to export, but the Spanish Post Office liked it so much that they adopted it as their standard domestic telephone.

AMBASSADOR

BT/GEC/DAVID CARTER

Designed by David Carter and made by GEC, the Ambassador was one of the first phones with a side-by-side design, as opposed to the traditional 'dog-and-bone' form. This became a standard format, which has subsequently been improved and re-designed right up to the present day, and also doubles as a wall phone.

ABS PLASTIC, 1986,
H4.5 X W5.75 X D9.5IN / H11.4 X W14.6 X D24.1CM

ASTROPHON
ERICSSON

As interiors became more functional, the style of the office and the domestic phone blended in a composite design. With a name suitable for the Space Age, the Astrophon was Ericsson's last model for the domestic market before specializing in office telecommunications.

ABS PLASTIC, 1982,
H4 X W8.5 X D7IN / H10.1 X W21.6 X D17.9CM

VISCOUNT
STC

One of the classic designs of the 1980s, the Viscount looked as good in the home as in the office. It could either sit on a table or be placed on the wall. This green version was unusual for its time, as the colourful 1970s had already given way to a vogue for more subdued colours.

ABS PLASTIC, 1987,
H8.7 X W9 X D3IN
H22 X W22.8 X D7.5CM

KIRK PLUS

KIRK TELECOM/STOCKHOLM
AND ZOREA

The term 'hanging up the phone' once again has meaning with the severely geometric 'Kirk Plus' (no relation to Captain Kirk) wall phone. A model of minimalism, designed by Marianne Stockholm and Gad Zorea, this phone expressed the best Danish design qualities and showed that new styles were still possible.

ABS PLASTIC, 1988,
H3 X W8 X D8IN / H7.6 X W20.3 X D20.3CM

SUPER BLOCK
TYCO/GLASS AND VOLPE

If form follows fun in the Post-Modern age, nothing could represent the philosophy better than this phone from the US toy company Tyco, aimed at the children's market but snapped up by light-hearted adults worldwide. The drawer in the side even contains some spare building blocks to enable the speaker to while away a tedious business conversation!

MIRIAM 100
OLIVETTI/SOWDEN
AND MORGAN

Continuing its reputation as a design leader, Olivetti commissioned George Sowden and Simon Morgan to design a telephone to add to their range of products. They created this elegant desk phone, of understated simplicity and beautifully balanced proportions.

SAN PLASTIC, 1988,
H4 X W7 X D8IN
H10 X W17.8 X D20.3CM

25

ABS PLASTIC, 1992,
H3 X W5 X D9IN / H7.6 X W12.7 X D22.8CM

ABS PLASTIC, 1992,
H2.75 X W8.75 X D6.5IN / H7 X W22.2 X D16.5CM

DUET 200

BT/RANDOM PRODUCT DESIGN

This was one of the three families of phone designed for BT (British Telecom), a publicly quoted company since 1984, by design consultants Random Product Design in 1992. A subtly sculptured phone with no hard edges, it was clearly intended for domestic (probably bedroom) use. The push-buttons were computer-designed, with a compound curve that minimizes fingernail contact.

RELATE 180

BT/RANDOM PRODUCT DESIGN

Under increased competition from other phone systems after deregulation, BT commissioned this new generic range of phones from the Random Product Design team. Chief designer Gus Desbarats acknowledges that the styling has a hint of the waisted Coca-Cola bottle. The Relate range included yet another attempt to perfect the video phone, but it still did not catch on.

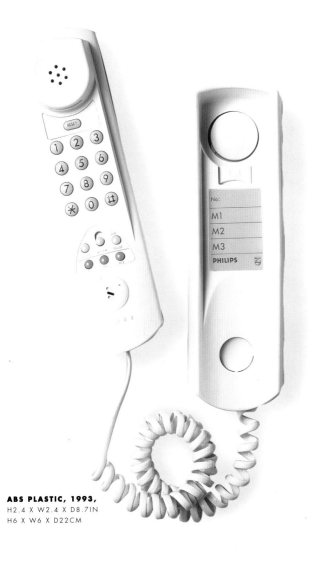

D9033

PHILIPS

D on Genaro at Henry Dreyfuss Associates changed the shape of telephones permanently when he created the 'gondola'-style Trimline for Bell Laboratories in 1968, and a host of telephone makers followed the trend. This neat one-piece phone, with the push-buttons now on the handpiece, typifies the minimalist and discreet look of a consciously sculpted, pleasant-to-handle phoneset.

ABS PLASTIC, 1993,
H2.4 X W2.4 X D8.7IN
H6 X W6 X D22CM

ABS PLASTIC, 1994,
H8.75 X W6 X D2.75IN
H22.2 X W15.2 X D7CM

LOTUS W
KIRK TELECOM/ STOCKHOLM AND ZOREA

Following in the stark style of their earlier designs for Kirk, Marianne Stockholm and Gad Zorea devised this handsomely functional wall phone, which has distinct minimalist, sculptural qualities. It is available in an arresting range of colour combinations that enhance the 'art-object' look – and in classic black.

SOFTPHONE

RECYCO INC./NICOLAI CANETTI

With this phone, software takes on a new meaning, but for stress relief at work or a child-proof instrument, what could make more sense? A classic example of irreverent product design, the Softphone takes advantage of the wonderful, easily coloured and resilient synthetic materials now available. But it does rather take the punch out of slamming down the receiver.

TX146

MORPHY RICHARDS/GLEN DIMPLEX DESIGN

Once a luxury item, the telephone has become both a necessity and an easily changed fashion accessory. The TX146 marks the return of the 'black box' (available only in black) and the 'dog-and-bone' layout, but in a smooth and carefully considered form. Technological advances bring a 'hands-free' phone that you don't even have to pick up!

ETHYL VINYL ACETATE ON ABS PLASTIC CASE, 1995,
H8.5 X W2.75 X D1.2IN
H21.5 X W7 X D2.6CM

ABS PLASTIC, 1995, H13.75 X W8 X D2.25IN / H35 X W20.3 X D5.7CM

PEPSIPHONE

P.F. PRODUCTS

Post-Modernism or nostalgia? If there is one trend that is evident in phone design in the late 1990s, it is that the telephone can resemble anything the customer wants it to. Here we see the return of the wall phone in a form that neither Bell nor Edison would have appreciated. The old-style Pepsi logo lights up when the phone rings.

SPOTLIGHT 753

MYBELLE

Transparent phones have occasionally been made in the past, but usually for promotional purposes only. Although other transparent gadgets have appeared since the 1970s, the idea of a see-through phone was a late arrival. The delightful Spotlight has a brightly coloured interior that reveals all the visually intriguing electronics that are usually hidden away.

FLORENTEEN

GEEMARC/MIK HOULDSWORTH

Given that teenagers can spend many hours on the phone, the next step is to encourage them to have one of their own. With its lime-green handset, matt black

base and tempting, Smartie-bright coloured buttons, the Florenteen is clearly aimed at the teenage market.

ABS PLASTIC, 1997,
H2.5 X W8.25 X D5.2IN / H6.3 X W20.9 X D13.2CM

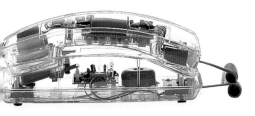

ABS PLASTIC, 1997,
H4 X W2.75 X D8.25IN
H10.2 X W7 X D21CM

ACKNOWLEDGEMENTS

The author would like to thank the following for their invaluable help and advice, and also for the loan of phones for photography as follows:

Brighton Communications: page 26 left, 30, 31 left

BT Museum: page 7 bottom left, 8 (all), 9 left, 10, 12 left and right, 15 right, 20, 22 right, 23 left and right, 26 right

General Dare: page 7 top left and right, 9 right, 11 left and right, 13, 14 left and right, 16 right, 17 right, 19 left, 21 right, 25 right

Henry Dreyfuss Associates: page 16 left, 17 left

Simon Fiegel: page 15 left

Geemarc Ltd: page 31 right

Anthony & Robin Gemmill: page 18, 32left

Ideo: page 22 left

Kirk Telecom: page 19 right, 24, 28

Chris & Carol McEwan: page 21 left

Morphy Richards Consumer Electronics: page 29 left

Recyco UK Ltd: page 29 right

Penny Sparke: page 25 left.

Endpapers: working drawings of the Compact phone by designer **David Carter**.

Special thanks to **Birgit Olesen Elkjaer**, **Neil Johannessen**, **Jack McGarvey**, **Martyn Rowlands** and **Jeremy Weiselberg**.

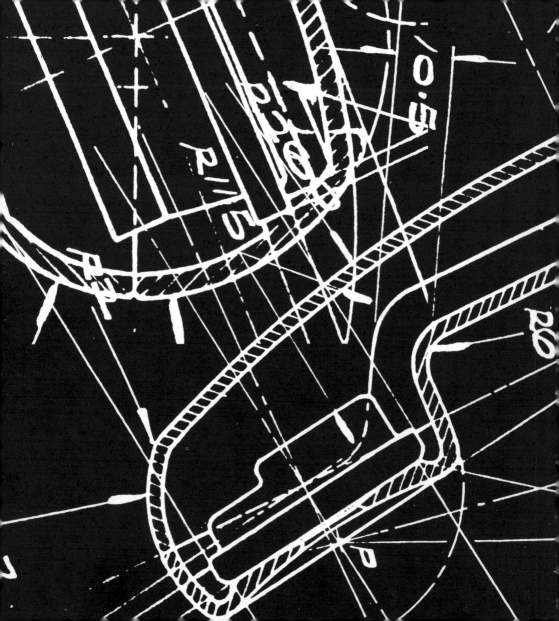